I Like School!
¡Me gusta la escuela!

by Deborah Schecter

ISBN: 978-1-338-70277-4
Illustrated by Anne Kennedy
Copyright © 2020 by Deborah Schecter. All rights reserved.
Published by Scholastic Inc., 557 Broadway, New York, NY 10012

10 9 8 7 6   68   23 24 25 26/0

Printed in Jiaxing, China. First printing, June 2020.

SCHOLASTIC

I like to read.

Me gusta leer.

I like to paint.

Me gusta pintar.

I like to cut.

Me gusta recortar.

I like to glue.

Me gusta pegar.

I like to count.

Me gusta contar.

I like to write.

Me gusta escribir.

I like school!

¡Me gusta la escuela!